Table of Contents

 Detective Work

Mark It!

1. b e d b u g
2. m a s c o t
3. c o b w e b
4. f a b r i c
5. u n z i p
6. h i c c u p
7. p i c n i c
8. r a d i s h
9. l i m i t
10. s u n t a n
11. t o p i c
12. u n l o c k

Read It!

1. unlock   picnic   fabric
2. bedbug   limit   suntan
3. topic   radish   unzip
4. mascot   cobweb   hiccup
5. limit   bedbug   unlock
6. suntan   mascot   topic
7. radish   hiccup   picnic

Challenging ⭐

	How many syllables?	🍎		🖐	🐙	☝
① robin	1　2					
② flip	1　2					
③ just	1　2					
④ cabin	1　2					

More Challenging ⭐⭐

	How many syllables?	🍎		🖐	🐙	☝
① swell	1　2					
② pickup	1　2					
③ tennis	1　2					
④ grass	1　2					

Most Challenging ⭐⭐⭐

	How many syllables?	🍎		🖐	🐙	☝
① unplug	1　2					
② blacktop	1　2					
③ strap	1　2					
④ milkman	1　2					

Phrases to Read ─────────────────────

Challenging ⭐

1. over the little cobweb
2. like the tennis match
3. robin would make a nest
4. then unzip her bag

More Challenging ⭐⭐

5. drink eggnog at the dentist
6. could give them hiccups
7. make up a good mascot
8. down into the big trashcan

Most Challenging ⭐⭐⭐

9. did not like it until Elvis came
10. would panic if the napkin fell
11. rush to find that satin rabbit
12. carry the pumpkin to the cabin

Sentences to Read

Challenging ☆

1. Edwin would make them finish. (5)

2. The mantis will sip the eggnog. (6)

3. My dog hiccups when she is glad. (7)

4. Ingrid would like a long fabric dress. (7)

More Challenging ☆☆

5. Cats dig around in the little radish patch. (8)

6. Calvin did not like the picnic until Sam came. (9)

7. Will you make me a relish and shrimp sandwich? (9)

8. Ride in the pickup truck with your mom and dad. (10)

Sentences to Read ————————————

Most Challenging ☆ ☆ ☆

⑨ Her mom will punish her if the bobsled gets lost. (10)

⑩ Tell Kevin to carry the pumpkin to the rustic cabin. (10)

⑪ Please put the sundress down into the big yellow trashcan. (10)

⑫ Jan will rush to the class to find her lost satin rabbit. (12)

Spell It!

Challenging Words ⭐

1st Syllable   2nd Syllable

1

2

3

4

5

More Challenging Words ⭐⭐

1st Syllable   2nd Syllable

1

2

3

4

5

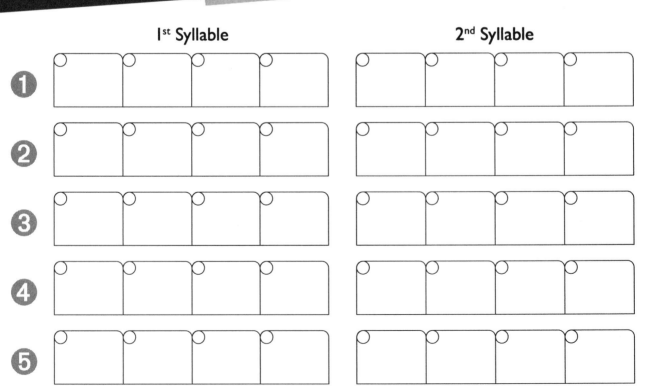

Mark It!

1. w e
2. h i
3. s o
4. m y
5. n o
6. b e
7. s h y
8. g o
9. s h e
10. t r y
11. h e
12. w h y

Read It!

1. we why hi
2. so my be
3. shy no she
4. go try he
5. be no hi
6. why she go
7. my so try

Challenging ⭐

	Syllable		Vowel Sound	
	Open	Closed	Long	Short
1 pro				
2 rug				
3 he				
4 go				

More Challenging ⭐ ☆

	Syllable		Vowel Sound	
	Open	Closed	Long	Short
1 best				
2 shy				
3 we				
4 no				

Most Challenging ⭐ ☆ ☆

	Syllable		Vowel Sound	
	Open	Closed	Long	Short
1 she				
2 rush				
3 glad				
4 be				

Challenging ☆

1. has come and go

2. catfish was so good

3. you and I jump into

4. credit to him and me

More Challenging ☆☆

5. no cobweb on his bathmat

6. she began to put the napkin

7. try the plastic one with him

8. why would the robin look

Most Challenging ☆☆☆

9. once they publish my long rabbit film

10. has to go try the pretty red laptop

11. look for the fly and the mantis

12. so you can put the big pumpkin into it

1 My big hiccups come and go. (6)

2 You and I jump into the fishpond. (7)

3 Try to put the nutmeg into your punch. (8)

4 He does not want to panic about the rat. (9)

More Challenging ★☆

5 My best subject is math; I like to subtract. (9)

6 There was no cobweb on his black bathmat. (8)

7 We will look for shellfish for the picnic at sunset. (10)

8 She has the red and green pompoms that go on my hat. (12)

Sentences to Read ————————————————— UNIT **16**

⑨ Go pick up the napkin that is on the plastic bench for him. (13)

⑩ The robin will fly down to look at the sapling in the grass. (13)

⑪ Stretch the bag so you can put the pumpkin into it for him. (13)

⑫ You could try the pretty red polish to match your dress for prom. (13)

Spell It!

UNIT **16**

Challenging Words ★

1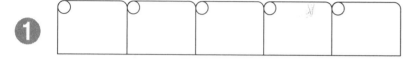

2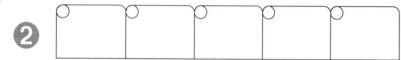

3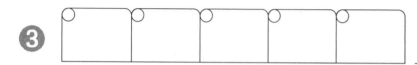

4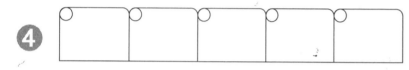

5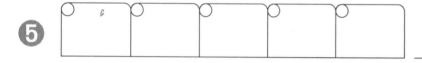

More Challenging Words ★ ★

1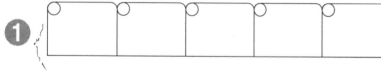

2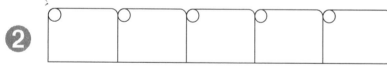

3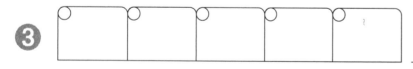

4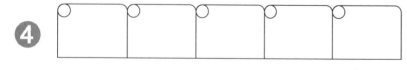

5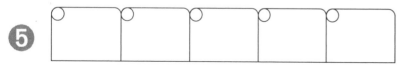

Detective Work

Mark It!

1. m o t e l
2. b a n j o
3. u n i t
4. r o b o t
5. b e g i n
6. m e n u

7. f o c u s
8. r e l a x
9. e v e n t
10. b a s i c
11. p r o t e c t
12. b e g a n

Read It!

1. banjo   focus   relax
2. begin   menu   protect
3. unit   relax   basic
4. motel   robot   unit
5. menu   banjo   event
6. began   motel   focus
7. basic   event   robot

 # Word Sort

UNIT 17

Challenging ⭐

	1st Syllable		2nd Syllable	
	Closed	Open	Closed	Open
❶ be•gan				
❷ den•tist				
❸ in•sect				
❹ pro•tect				

More Challenging ⭐⭐

	1st Syllable		2nd Syllable	
	Closed	Open	Closed	Open
❶ pump•kin				
❷ lim•it				
❸ ro•bot				
❹ jum•bo				

Most Challenging ⭐⭐⭐

	1st Syllable		2nd Syllable	
	Closed	Open	Closed	Open
❶ man•tis				
❷ de•pend				
❸ fo•cus				
❹ un•zip				

14   © 2014 Really Great Reading Company, LLC

Challenging ☆

1 beyond the picnic

2 take over the menu

3 go see the baking contest

4 could go to the motel

More Challenging ☆☆

5 tasting the best sandwich

6 focus on the chipmunk

7 take that jumbo fish

8 could begin to try tennis

Most Challenging ☆☆☆

9 where to sing classic music

10 credit the program to David

11 see six zigzags in the text

12 depends on where the cabin is

Challenging ☆

1 Take a look over the long menu. (7)

2 The contest will begin right now! (6)

3 Which program would you like to try? (7)

4 Did you see the planet Venus up there? (8)

More Challenging ☆ ☆

5 When you focus on the test, you can pass. (9)

6 I could go to the motel when the picnic is over. (11)

7 Going camping will depend on if we have a cabin. (10)

8 It is too humid to go get a suntan by the fishpond. (12)

Sentences to Read

Most Challenging ★ ★ ☆

⑨ My mom will always sing classic music before lunch. (9)

⑩ Where can you buy a shrimp sandwich by the hotel? (10)

⑪ My dad and I will take the jumbo catfish to the pond. (12)

⑫ Sam could begin to play tennis with the pro at the shop. (12)

Spell It! ———————————————————— UNIT 17

Challenging Words ⭐

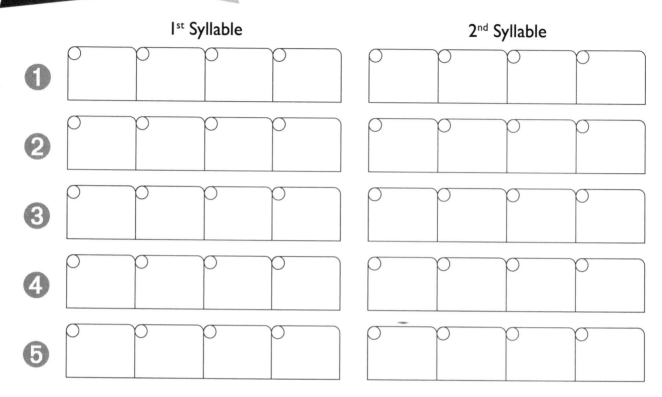

1st Syllable   2nd Syllable

1
2
3
4
5

More Challenging Words ⭐⭐

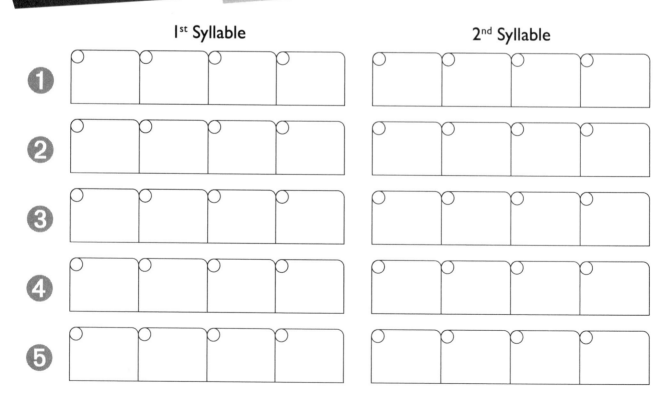

1st Syllable   2nd Syllable

1
2
3
4
5

Detective Work

Mark It!

1. w a g o n
2. s a n d a l
3. z e b r a
4. s e v e n
5. f r o z e n
6. d r a g o n
7. t u n n e l
8. b a c o n
9. p i l o t
10. m i n u s
11. e x t r a
12. a d u l t

Read It!

1. adult   frozen   pilot
2. bacon   extra   wagon
3. sandal   seven   minus
4. zebra   tunnel   dragon
5. frozen   bacon   seven
6. minus   wagon   zebra
7. extra   dragon   sandal

Challenging

	1st Syllable		2nd Syllable		Schwa?
	Closed	Open	Closed	Open	
1 ba•con					
2 e•vent					
3 a•dopt					
4 bro•ken					

More Challenging

	1st Syllable		2nd Syllable		Schwa?
	Closed	Open	Closed	Open	
1 men•u					
2 pand•a					
3 lem•on					
4 se•cret					

Most Challenging

	1st Syllable		2nd Syllable		Schwa?
	Closed	Open	Closed	Open	
1 blan•ket					
2 hu•man					
3 mas•cot					
4 mam•mal					

Phrases to Read

1 around any old zebra

2 can pet any little kitten here

3 to look for the red dragon

4 napkin for the crisp bacon

More Challenging ☆☆

5 be silent for a second

6 in the frozen lemon punch

7 model the classic dress here

8 saw the nickel on the red blanket

Most Challenging ☆☆☆

9 about to travel to the rocket contest

10 open your pocket to find a soft pretzel

11 will not eat an old, rotten melon for lunch

12 because the children could not find the mitten here

Sentences to Read

1 The chicken for lunch is still frozen. (7)

2 You can ask about crisp bacon here. (7)

3 My mom put on an apron for baking. (8)

4 Skip around the camel and the old zebra. (8)

More Challenging ☆ ☆

5 Can I have any extra frozen mango punch? (8)

6 Even the old panda sits here on the broken bench. (10)

7 Bella will chat about the little kitten until her dad comes. (11)

8 The nickel I saw on the red blanket is for David. (11)

9 Jackson will travel here for the contest in a big blue wagon. (12)

10 I ate a cactus and spinach sandwich with a small salad. (11)

11 Will you model the classic dress you saw in the closet? (11)

12 Emma ate a lemon and an old, rotten melon before lunch today. (12)

Challenging Words ⭐

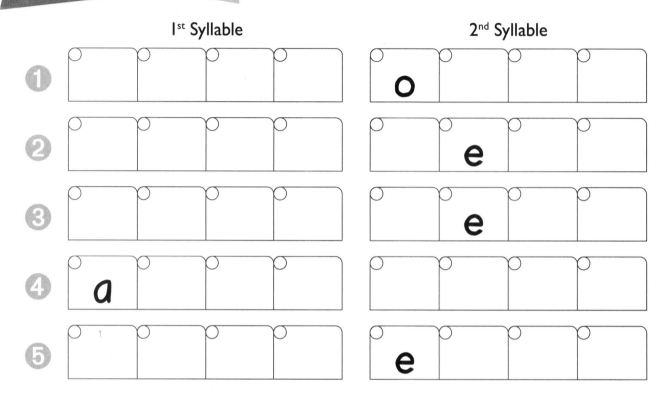

1ˢᵗ Syllable | 2ⁿᵈ Syllable

1. ▢▢▢▢ | o▢▢▢
2. ▢▢▢▢ | ▢e▢▢
3. ▢▢▢▢ | ▢e▢▢
4. a▢▢▢ | ▢▢▢▢
5. ▢▢▢▢ | e▢▢▢

More Challenging Words ⭐⭐

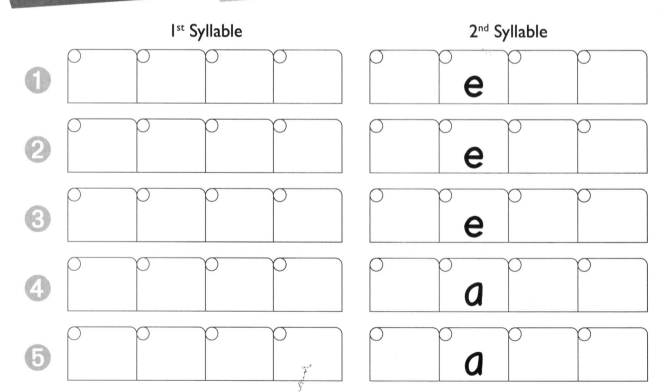

1ˢᵗ Syllable | 2ⁿᵈ Syllable

1. ▢▢▢▢ | ▢e▢▢
2. ▢▢▢▢ | ▢e▢▢
3. ▢▢▢▢ | ▢e▢▢
4. ▢▢▢▢ | ▢e▢▢
5. ▢▢▢▢ | ▢a▢▢

Detective Work

Mark It!

1. b a k e
2. f i n e
3. n o t e
4. p l a t e
5. s m i l e
6. w h a l e
7. k i t e
8. l a k e
9. g l o b e
10. c u t e
11. g r a p e
12. b r o k e

Read It!

1. bake   broke   whale
2. globe   cute   fine
3. note   plate   grape
4. lake   whale   smile
5. grape   fine   bake
6. plate   note   kite
7. smile   broke   cute

25

Word Sort

Challenging ☆

	Syllable			Vowel Phoneme	
	Closed	Open	VCE	Long	Short
① date					
② we					
③ tin					
④ cone					

More Challenging ☆ ☆

	Syllable			Vowel Phoneme	
	Closed	Open	VCE	Long	Short
① drive					
② go					
③ cube					
④ plan					

Most Challenging ☆ ☆ ☆

	Syllable			Vowel Phoneme	
	Closed	Open	VCE	Long	Short
① scrap					
② quake					
③ slime					
④ fly					

Challenging ☆

1. cut down the pine

2. bake the lemon cake

3. spoke about the long, fake note

4. with the very cute kitten

More Challenging ☆☆

5. made a little grape cake

6. was very late for our date

7. ate the snack on his plate

8. drove over the traffic cone in her lane

Most Challenging ☆☆☆

9. name the long game after Sam

10. if you ask us to use the jumbo kite

11. smile about the little melon basket

12. shine the lamp over the broken game

❶ Cut down the pine by the lake. (7)

❷ Ask to fly a little kite at home. (8)

❸ The fake note made Nate mad. (6)

❹ Pete came over to jump rope with Dave. (8)

More Challenging ☆ ☆

❺ Bake a little lemon cake for the bride. (8)

❻ His very good grade on the long test gave him hope. (11)

❼ Jane went into the kitchen to look at the shape of the cake. (12)

❽ Mike will ask you to name the state with this long shape. (12)

Most Challenging ★ ★ ☆

9 I want to try the kale from the new menu. (10)

10 Iris will tell us to use the jumbo kite in Tampa. (11)

11 The secret cave is a very warm home for the panda. (11)

12 The oval lamp was broken when it fell over after the small quake. (13)

Spell It!

Challenging Words ⭐

1.
2.
3.
4.
5.

More Challenging Words ⭐⭐

1.
2.
3.
4.
5.

Mark It!

1. p a n c a k e
2. b a t h r o b e
3. i n v i t e
4. r e p t i l e
5. s u n s h i n e
6. t a d p o l e
7. w i s h b o n e
8. l i f e t i m e
9. p o l i t e
10. l u n c h t i m e
11. v o l u m e
12. m i l k s h a k e

Read It!

1. milkshake | volume | tadpole
2. lunchtime | wishbone | pancake
3. bathrobe | sunshine | reptile
4. invite | pancake | lifetime
5. tadpole | polite | lunchtime
6. lifetime | milkshake | volume
7. reptile | bathrobe | wishbone

 # Word Sort

Challenging

	1st Syllable			2nd Syllable			
	Closed	Open	VCE	Closed	Open	VCE	Schwa?

1 e•rase

2 fish•bone

3 pa•rade

4 cave•man

More Challenging

	1st Syllable			2nd Syllable			
	Closed	Open	VCE	Closed	Open	VCE	Schwa?

1 lo•cate

2 re•mote

3 cup•cake

4 base•ment

Most Challenging

	1st Syllable			2nd Syllable			
	Closed	Open	VCE	Closed	Open	VCE	Schwa?

1 a•maze

2 hand•shake

3 be•came

4 rock•slide

Challenging ☆

1. became too late

2. a good cupcake

3. every handmade gift

4. too selfish right around lunchtime

More Challenging ☆☆

5. on a picnic in the sunshine

6. gaze at the lamp by my bedside

7. use the button to mute the volume

8. know how to make a good milkshake

Most Challenging ☆☆☆

9. could be the best athlete in Flagstaff

10. reptile sits around on a rock in the sunshine

11. went inside the little cave with the firemen

12. every kid will know how to play the trombone

❶ It became too late to drive home. (7)

❷ We will go on a picnic in the sunshine. (9)

❸ There was a note on every handmade gift. (8)

❹ Where can I get a good cupcake around here? (9)

More Challenging ☆ ☆

❺ I have to take a nap right around lunchtime. (9)

❻ Can you press the mute button on the remote? (9)

❼ Come inside where there is cake and good music too. (10)

❽ Do you know how to make a good, thick milkshake? (10)

Most Challenging ⭐⭐☆

⑨ Jake saw a small tadpole and four catfish in the local pond. (12)

⑩ There were too many men standing under the metal trapeze. (10)

⑪ The upset reptile will take a rest on a rock in the sunshine. (13)

⑫ Every kid in class will know how to play the trombone and the trumpet too. (15)

Spell It!

Challenging Words ☆

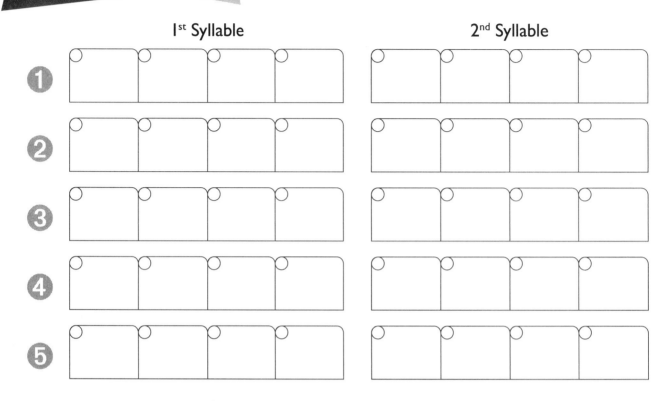

1st Syllable	2nd Syllable
①	
②	
③	
④	
⑤	

More Challenging Words ☆ ☆

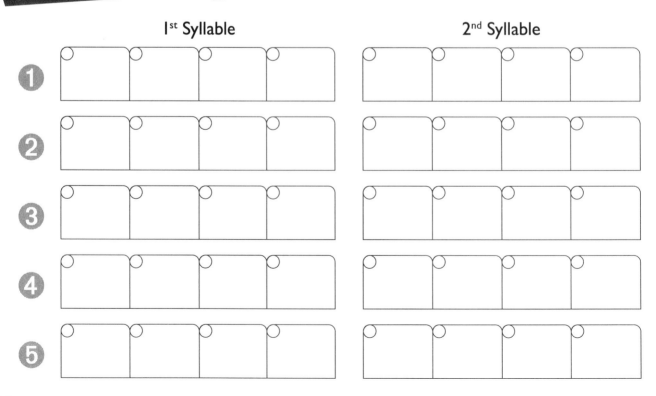

1st Syllable	2nd Syllable
①	
②	
③	
④	
⑤	

Mark It!

①	b e a d		⑦	m a y
②	g r e e n		⑧	b e e t
③	d a y		⑨	c l e a n
④	g a i n		⑩	t e e n
⑤	s e a t		⑪	m e a n
⑥	r a i n		⑫	p l a y

Read It!

①	play	day	beet
②	rain	clean	green
③	gain	seat	teen
④	mean	bead	day
⑤	may	beet	play
⑥	bead	mean	gain
⑦	teen	may	seat

Word Sort

Challenging ☆

	How many syllables?	1st Syllable			2nd Syllable		
		Closed	Open	Vowel Team	Closed	Open	Vowel Team
1 team	1　2						
2 delay	1　2						
3 repeat	1　2						
4 pray	1　2						

More Challenging ☆☆

	How many syllables?	1st Syllable			2nd Syllable		
		Closed	Open	Vowel Team	Closed	Open	Vowel Team
1 fail	1　2						
2 reread	1　2						
3 cheek	1　2						
4 email	1　2						

Most Challenging ☆☆☆

	How many syllables?	1st Syllable			2nd Syllable		
		Closed	Open	Vowel Team	Closed	Open	Vowel Team
1 sixteen	1　2						
2 cheerful	1　2						
3 trail	1　2						
4 complain	1　2						

Phrases to Read

Challenging ☆

1. eat a Greek salad

2. has a mean streak

3. going to be a gray day

4. mail came after lunchtime

More Challenging ☆☆

5. need to email the team

6. don't think about the stain

7. going to stay and play after

8. playful and pretty like Gail and Jean

Most Challenging ☆☆☆

9. prepay to see the screenplay

10. agreed on getting the pretty, green tree

11. happy queen went away to think

12. think about candy as a treat after our meal

Challenging ☆

1 Gail went away to eat her Greek salad. (8)

2 I think Bob has a pretty mean streak. (8)

3 It is going to be a very gray day. (9)

4 The gray rockfish will not swim upstream. (7)

More Challenging ☆ ☆

5 Candy is a treat, but not after every meal. (9)

6 I am going to email the team after the play. (10)

7 The pup is very playful like Gail and Jean. (9)

8 The lady is going to stay and play in the rain. (11)

9 Will Jean reveal the stain on her pretty pants? (9)

10 Just between you and me, I think Mandy is sweet. (10)

11 The pretty queen went away to Tulsa to get some beets. (11)

12 The mail came to the campsite after lunchtime. (8)

Spell It!

Challenging Words ⭐

1

2

3

4

5

More Challenging Words ⭐⭐

1st Syllable	2nd Syllable

1

2

3

4

5

Detective Work

Mark It!

1. c o a t
2. r i g h t
3. l o a f
4. s i g h t
5. o a k
6. h i g h
7. s o a p
8. f l o a t
9. b r i g h t
10. g o a t
11. n i g h t
12. l o a d

Read It!

1. right   loaf   bright
2. sight   oak   soap
3. high   float   night
4. soap   goat   oak
5. bright   sight   loaf
6. night   load   high
7. coat   right   float

Challenging ☆

	How many syllables?	1st Syllable			2nd Syllable		
		Closed	Open	Vowel Team	Closed	Open	Vowel Team
① light	1 2						
② busload	1 2						
③ road	1 2						
④ highest	1 2						

More Challenging ☆☆

	How many syllables?	1st Syllable			2nd Syllable		
		Closed	Open	Vowel Team	Closed	Open	Vowel Team
① bright	1 2						
② cocoa	1 2						
③ daylight	1 2						
④ soak	1 2						

Most Challenging ☆☆☆

	How many syllables?	1st Syllable			2nd Syllable		
		Closed	Open	Vowel Team	Closed	Open	Vowel Team
① highway	1 2						
② toast	1 2						
③ upload	1 2						
④ raincoat	1 2						

Challenging ☆

1. might fight again

2. kids who play at night

3. walk down the road

4. might have been lost

More Challenging ☆☆

5. coach the team again

6. a busload of children at night

7. walk in right before the contest

8. before sleeping in the boat again

Most Challenging ☆☆☆

9. do not like foamy coffee

10. been to the highest peak

11. who reload the coal in the pit

12. walk to see the tugboat before daylight

Sentences to Read

Challenging ☆

1 My cat and dog might fight again. (7)

2 Is there oatmeal stuck in your throat? (7)

3 Look for toads when you walk down the road. (9)

4 My dad will coach the swimming team again. (8)

More Challenging ☆ ☆

5 The busload of children was going on a trip. (9)

6 Can you float on your right side for five seconds? (10)

7 Calvin might have been lost if Ida had not come. (10)

8 Who can lend me a raincoat until I locate mine? (10)

Most Challenging ★ ★ ☆

⑨ Iris has been to the highest peak in Texas three times. (11)

⑩ Who will take me out on a speedboat before May? (10)

⑪ We drove on the highway before getting to the contest. (10)

⑫ Let's take a walk before daylight when it will be too hot. (12)

Spell It!

UNIT **22**

Challenging Words ☆

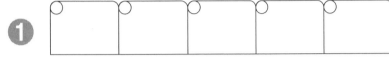

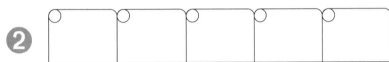

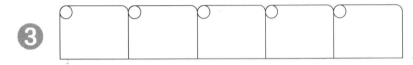

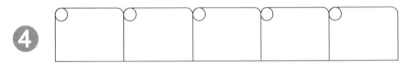

More Challenging Words ☆☆

1st Syllable   2nd Syllable

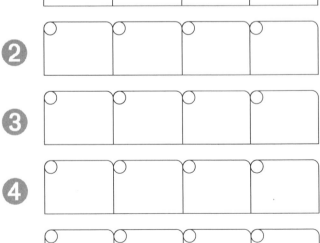

Detective Work

UNIT **23**

Mark It!

1. l a s t e d
2. s p e l l e d
3. m e l t e d
4. m a i l e d
5. b r u s h e d
6. d u s t e d
7. i t c h e d
8. l i f t e d
9. l o c k e d
10. e n d e d
11. s o a k e d
12. p e e l e d

Read It!

1. soaked   melted   lifted
2. dusted   locked   peeled
3. mailed   brushed   ended
4. peeled   lasted   melted
5. spelled   lifted   soaked
6. lasted   locked   mailed
7. ended   itched   brushed

© 2014 Really Great Reading Company, LLC **49**

Word Sort

Challenging

	How many syllables?		Adds syllable /ed/	Adds sound /d/ or /t/
1 packed	1	2		
2 tested	1	2		
3 checked	1	2		
4 waited	1	2		

More Challenging

	How many syllables?		Adds syllable /ed/	Adds sound /d/ or /t/
1 cheated	1	2		
2 spilled	1	2		
3 dented	1	2		
4 matched	1	2		

Most Challenging

	How many syllables?		Adds syllable /ed/	Adds sound /d/ or /t/
1 smashed	1	2		
2 printed	1	2		
3 sailed	1	2		
4 toasted	1	2		

Phrases to Read

Challenging ☆

1 picked up your own soap

2 plane landed at midnight

3 toasted his own bagel

4 ducked only when the ball came

More Challenging ☆☆

5 fluffed the only blanket on the bed

6 the only frosted treat that melted

7 always itched the bright red rash

8 tossed the cracked lamp in the trash

Most Challenging ☆☆☆

9 always goes away when he is yelled at

10 rushed to help because the lady screamed

11 drilled a hole and fixed the broken frame

12 cleaned because Brady spilled his own milk

❶ The sloppy kid always gulped down his milk. (8)

❷ Steve smashed the vase when he dusted it. (8)

❸ Faith brushed the bug off the slanted desk. (8)

❹ We waited because the baby spilled her cup. (8)

More Challenging ☆ ☆

❺ Cade always goes away when he is yelled at. (9)

❻ The game ended when Brenda tossed the only ball away. (10)

❼ They bumped into me when they rushed to catch the bus. (11)

❽ The teen dashed home after the plane landed at midnight. (10)

⑨ David fussed because his only frozen treat melted in the sun. (11)

⑩ Bobby drilled a hole and fixed the broken frame on his own. (12)

⑪ Granny always fluffed the quilt and checked that the sheets were clean. (12)

⑫ It is only right to fix it on your own if you dented it. (14)

Spell It!

Challenging Words ☆

1

2

3

4

5

More Challenging Words ☆ ☆

1st Syllable	2nd Syllable

1

2

3

4

5

Detective Work ──────────── UNIT 24

Mark It!

1. t a l l e r
2. e n d e d
3. a c t e d
4. b o x e s
5. s p e n d i n g
6. r e n t e d
7. p a t c h e s
8. b r i g h t e r
9. b o a t i n g
10. s m a l l e r
11. p a c k i n g
12. s w e e t e r

Read It!

1. patches   packing   brighter
2. rented   boating   sweeter
3. boxes   patches   ended
4. spending   taller   acted
5. packing   rented   smaller
6. taller   acted   boxes
7. smaller   boating   spending

   55

Challenging ⭐

	-er	-ed	-s	-es	-ing

1 faster
2 days
3 buzzes
4 ended

More Challenging ⭐⭐

	-er	-ed	-s	-es	-ing

1 rushed
2 treats
3 richer
4 sending

Most Challenging ⭐⭐⭐

	-er	-ed	-s	-es	-ing

1 lasted
2 trains
3 fighting
4 beaches

Phrases to Read

Challenging ☆

1 planted all our roses

2 both write our names

3 higher than the tallest one

4 does not like eating grapes

More Challenging ☆☆

5 teaches him how to be a singer

6 give the boxes to the helper

7 likes both painting and singing

8 when our sailboat drifted faster

Most Challenging ☆☆☆

9 fussed while itching his rashes

10 trusted the teacher to write the notes

11 a singer who does not like acting

12 give mashed peaches to the baby

Challenging ☆

➊ We both like painting but not singing. (7)

➋ My teacher asked us to write our names. (8)

➌ Does the baby have rashes on her legs? (8)

➍ Give all the packed boxes to the helper. (8)

More Challenging ☆☆

➎ The ball player is much taller than the children. (9)

➏ Patty trusted us both until we messed up her kitchen. (10)

➐ Does he bake batches of treats to give to his classmates? (11)

➑ We both screamed when our sailboats hit the rocks. (9)

Most Challenging ☆ ☆ ☆

⑨ The bee buzzes when it reaches the patch of roses. (10)

⑩ We will write our essays and keep them in the locked desk. (12)

⑪ The crutches helped him walk after he fell playing baseball. (10)

⑫ If we study for the tests, our teacher will be happy. (11)

Spell It!

1st Syllable   2nd Syllable

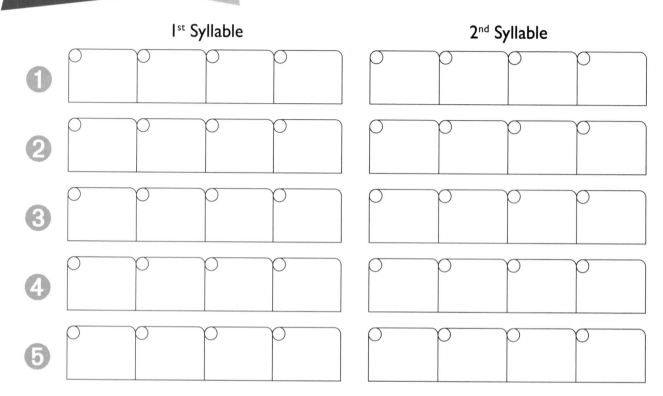

More Challenging Words ☆ ☆

1st Syllable   2nd Syllable

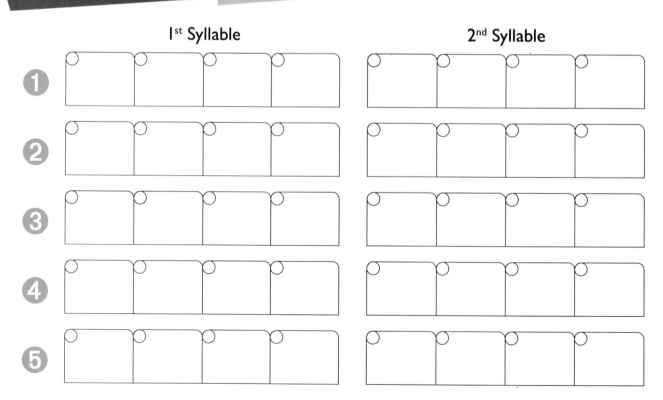

Mark It!

1. s o a k
2. m a t c h
3. f r o s t
4. s e a t
5. f i g h t
6. s t a y

7. b u n c h
8. d r e s s
9. b r u s h
10. p l a i n
11. t r e a t
12. c h e e k

Read It!

1. match   plain   bunch
2. stay   soak   brush
3. fight   plain   seat
4. frost   bunch   match
5. treat   cheek   fight
6. dress   stay   cheek
7. soak   treat   frost

Word Sort

Challenging ☆

	1st Syllable				2nd Syllable				Schwa?
	Closed	Open	VCE	Vowel Team	Closed	Open	VCE	Vowel Team	
① a•lone									
② cup•cake									
③ so•fa									
④ chip•munk									

More Challenging ☆☆

	1st Syllable				2nd Syllable				Schwa?
	Closed	Open	VCE	Vowel Team	Closed	Open	VCE	Vowel Team	
① ho•tel									
② coast•line									
③ mis•take									
④ jum•bo									

Most Challenging ☆☆☆

	1st Syllable				2nd Syllable				Schwa?
	Closed	Open	VCE	Vowel Team	Closed	Open	VCE	Vowel Team	
① a•maze									
② pave•ment									
③ flash•light									
④ space•ship									

© 2014 Really Great Reading Company, LLC

Challenging ☆

1. likes to read and write

2. fell asleep before bedtime

3. patches on her green pants

4. chicken clucked until midnight

More Challenging ☆☆

5. grilled the meat for the picnic

6. rested with the baby all night

7. plays the trombone in the band

8. makes him bring his raincoat and hat

Most Challenging ☆☆☆

9. translate the notes into Spanish

10. dug up the weeds to plant roses

11. use sunscreen to play at the beach

12. likes peaches but not green bean salad

Challenging ☆

① Pete grilled the meat for the picnic. (7)

② We planted the beans next to the wheat. (8)

③ Tommy went sailing in the tugboat with Joan. (8)

④ The teacher does not like kids eating in class. (9)

More Challenging ☆☆

⑤ Be brave and fly higher than the tallest tree. (9)

⑥ Bring sunscreen if you will be playing at the beach. (10)

⑦ Jake, did your mom put green patches on your pants? (10)

⑧ Did you know that Shay plays the trombone in the band? (11)

9 Rose will translate the notes into Spanish for her classmate. (10)

10 Bring your raincoat and hat if you want to splash in the street. (13)

11 The band played jazz music at the request of the kings and queens. (13)

12 Dad rested with the baby when he woke up at midnight. (11)

Challenging Words ⭐

1.
2.
3.
4.
5.

More Challenging Words ⭐⭐

1st Syllable   2nd Syllable

1.
2.
3.
4.
5.

My Heart Words

			♡ full	♡ hot
♡ a	♡ best	♡ do	♡ funny	♡ how
♡ about	♡ better	♡ does	♡ gave	♡ hurt
♡ after	♡ big	♡ done	♡ get	♡ I
♡ again	♡ black	♡ don't	♡ give	♡ if
♡ all	♡ blue	♡ down	♡ go	♡ in
♡ always	♡ both	♡ draw	♡ goes	♡ into
♡ am	♡ bring	♡ drink	♡ going	♡ is
♡ an	♡ brown	♡ eat	♡ good	♡ it
♡ and	♡ but	♡ eight	♡ got	♡ its
♡ any	♡ buy	♡ every	♡ green	♡ jump
♡ are	♡ by	♡ fall	♡ grow	♡ just
♡ around	♡ call	♡ far	♡ had	♡ keep
♡ as	♡ came	♡ fast	♡ has	♡ kind
♡ ask	♡ can	♡ find	♡ have	♡ know
♡ at	♡ carry	♡ first	♡ he	♡ laugh
♡ ate	♡ clean	♡ five	♡ help	♡ let
♡ away	♡ cold	♡ fly	♡ her	♡ light
♡ be	♡ come	♡ for	♡ here	♡ like
♡ because	♡ could	♡ found	♡ him	♡ little
♡ been	♡ cut	♡ four	♡ his	♡ live
♡ before	♡ did	♡ from	♡ hold	♡ long